THE DEFINITI

John Barry

CW00434410

COLLECTION

IMP

International
MUSIC
Publications

Compiled by Ulf Klenfeldt
Cover Design: London Advertising Partnership
Published 2000

© International Music Publications Limited
Griffin House 161 Hammersmith Road London W6 8BS England

Born Free (from *Born Free*)

Words by Don Black
Music by John Barry

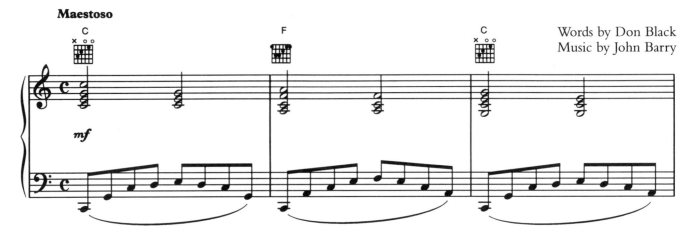

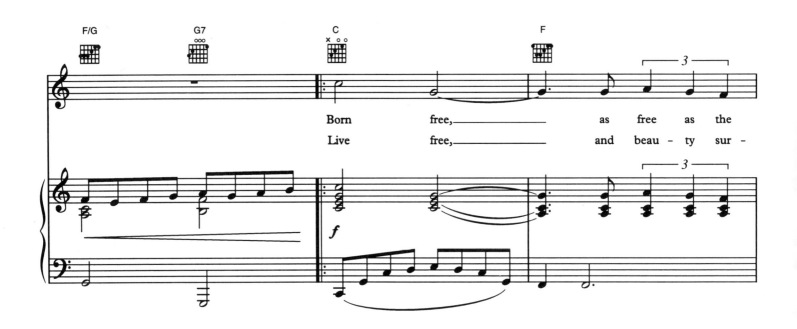

roar - ing tide so there's no need to____ hide._____

Born free,_____ and life is worth liv - - ing,_____ but on - ly worth

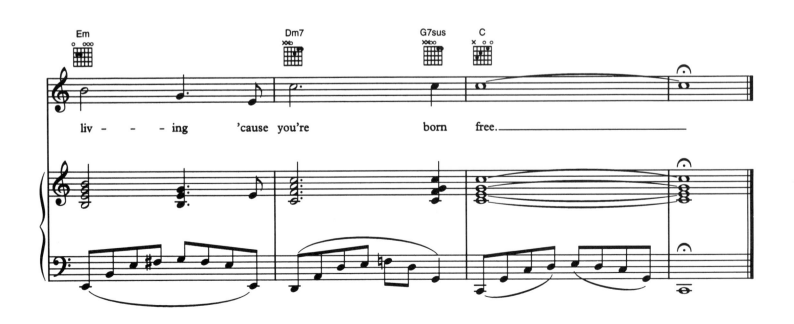

liv - - ing 'cause you're born free._____

The Beyondness Of Things
(from *The Beyondness Of Things*)

Music by John Barry

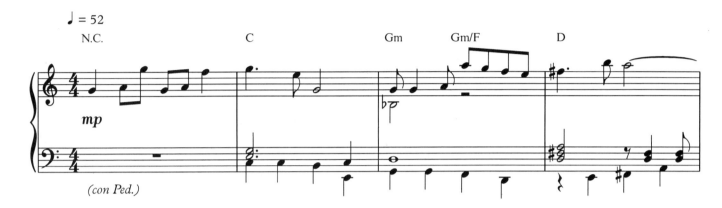

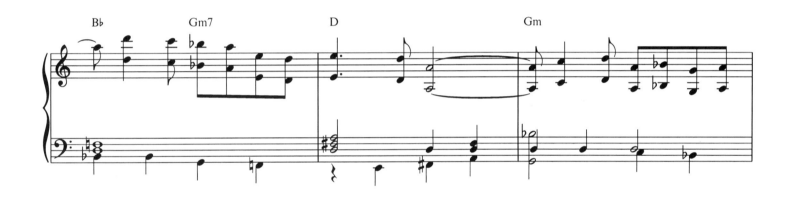

Dance With Reality
(from *The Beyondness Of Things*)

Music by John Barry

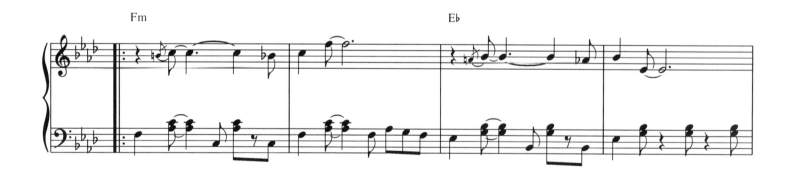

Dances With Wolves (Main Theme)

Words and Music by John Barry

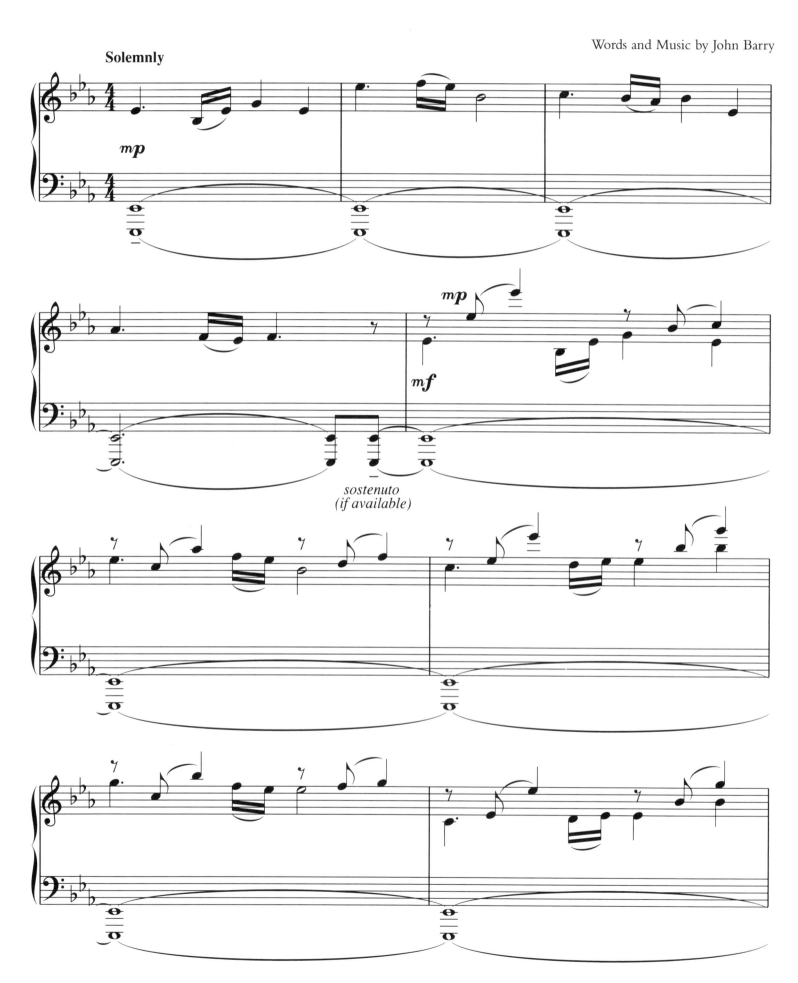

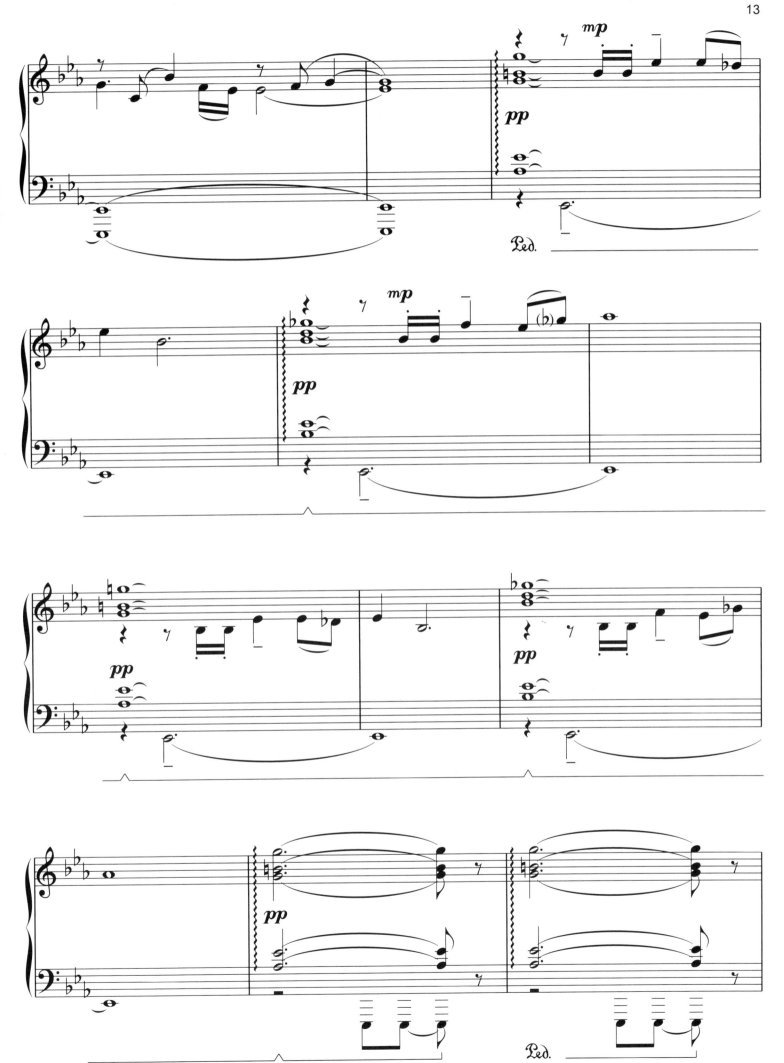

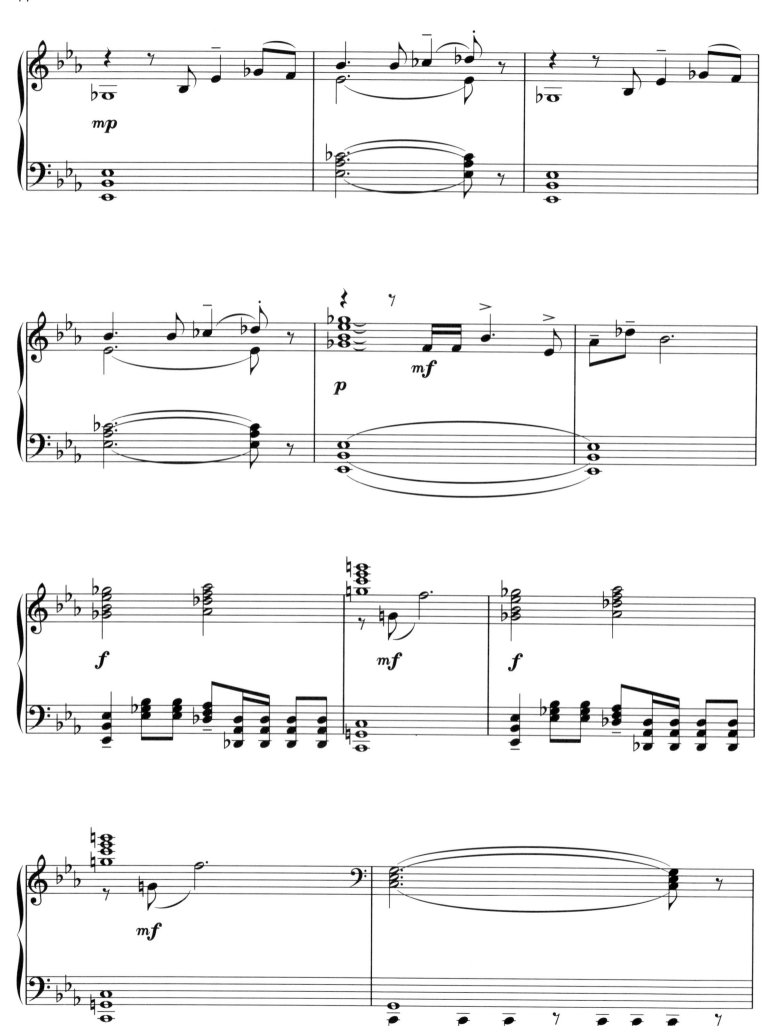

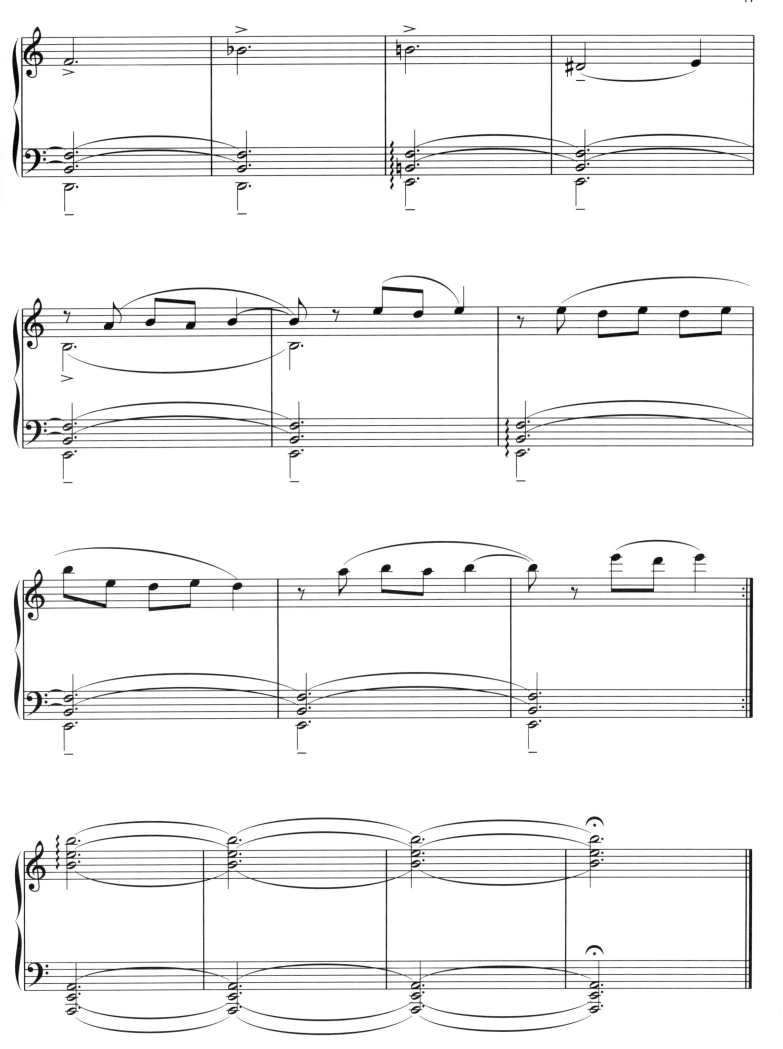

In All The Right Places
(from *Indecent Proposal*)

Words by Lisa Stansfield
Music by John Barry

Moderate rock ♩ = 92

(with pedal)

If you take me straight to heav-en, I could nev-er fall.__

'Cause lov-ing you is what I'm made for, I'd glad-ly give my all-in-all.__

It does-n't mat-ter where__ I am,__ as long as I'm with you.__

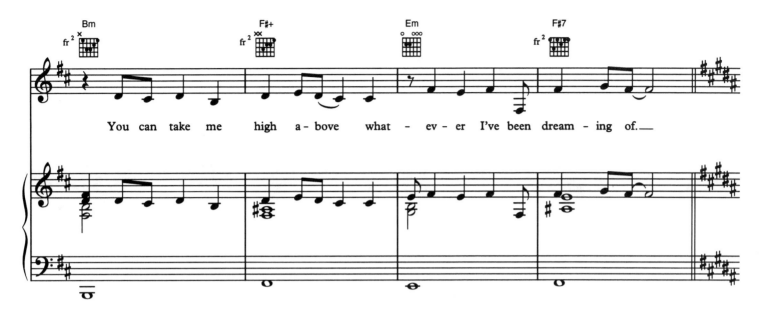

You can take me high a - bove what - ev - er I've been dream - ing of.___

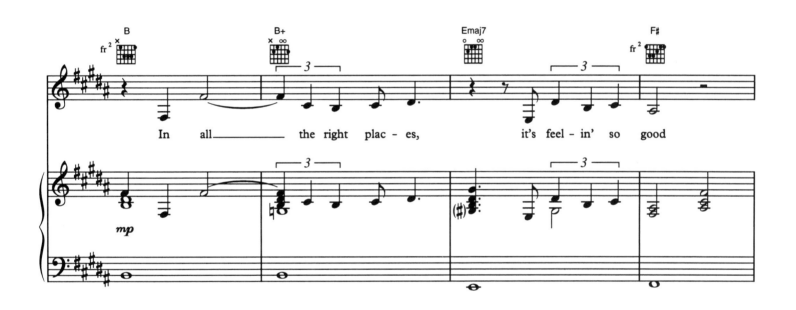

In all_____ the right plac - es, it's feel - in' so good

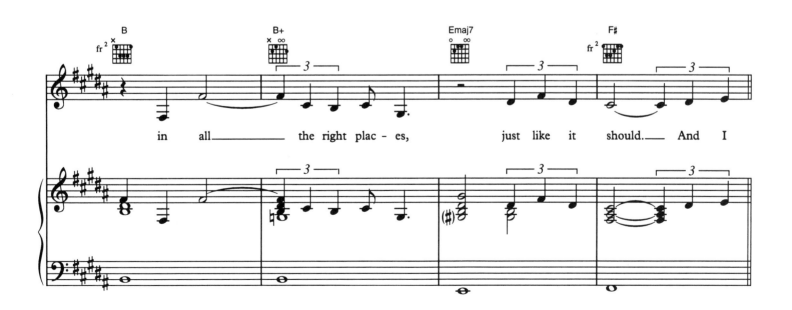

in all_____ the right plac - es, just like it should.___ And I

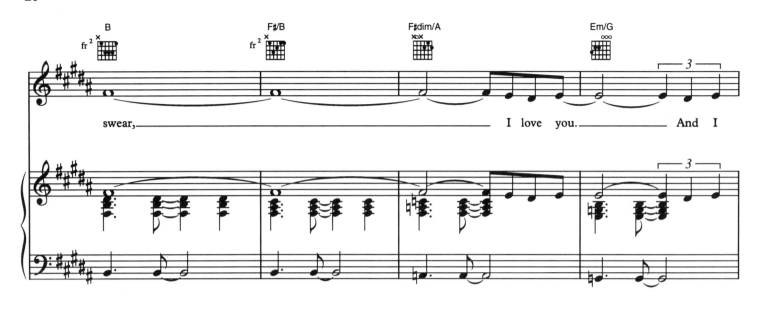

swear,＿＿＿＿＿＿＿＿＿＿＿＿＿＿＿＿＿＿＿＿ I love you.＿＿＿＿ And I

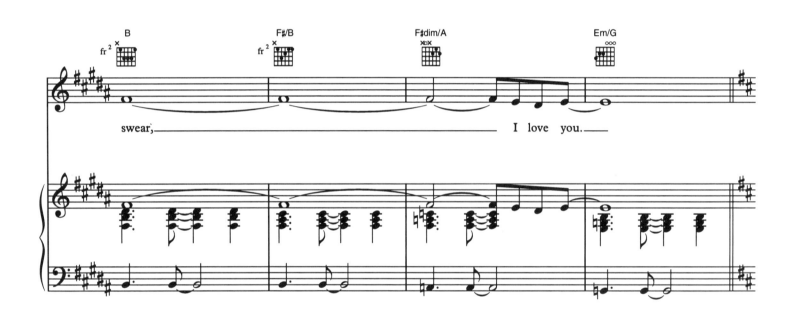

swear,＿＿＿＿＿＿＿＿＿＿＿＿＿＿＿＿＿＿＿＿＿ I love you.＿＿＿

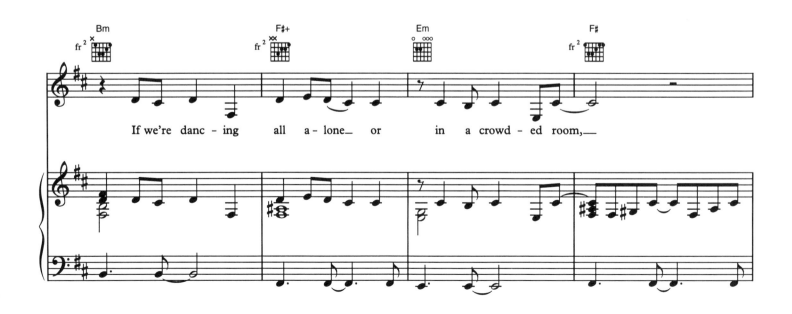

If we're danc - ing all a - lone＿ or in a crowd - ed room,＿

when you wrap your arms a - round me, you al -ways send me to the moon.

When we kiss our sug - ar kiss - es and the mu - sic starts to play,—

we've got love, we've got each oth - er and we're go - in' all the way.

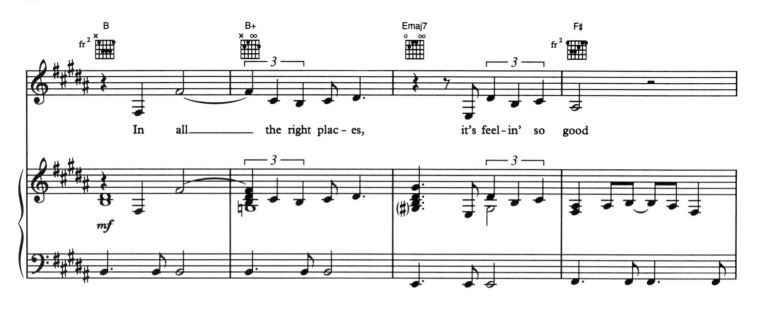

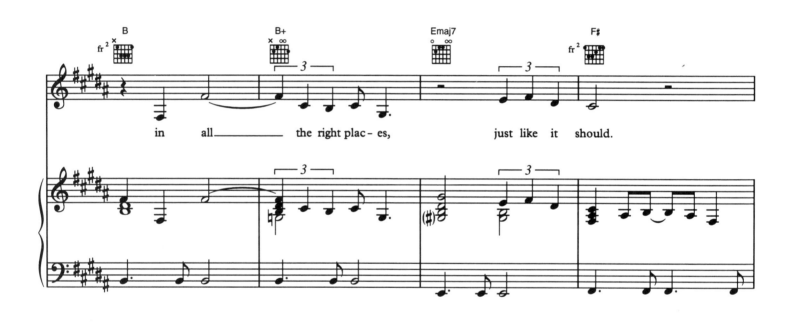

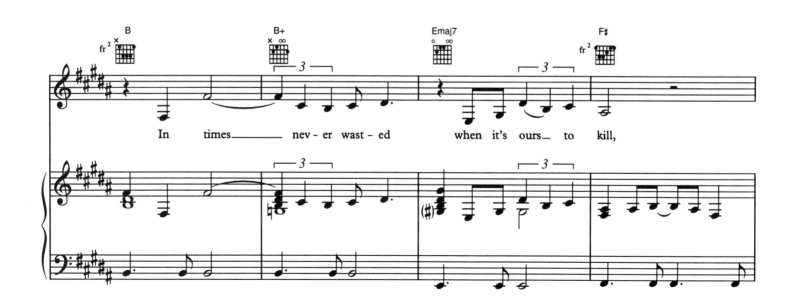

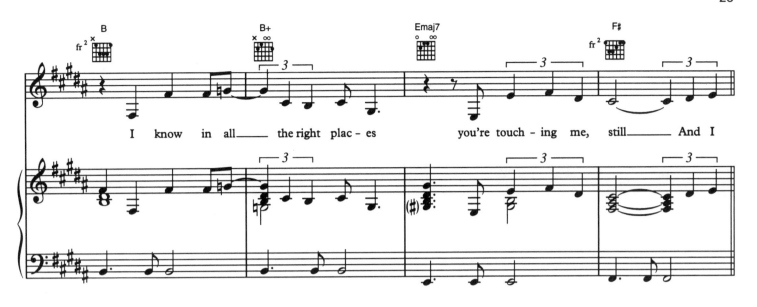

I know in all____ the right plac - es   you're touch - ing me, still____ And I

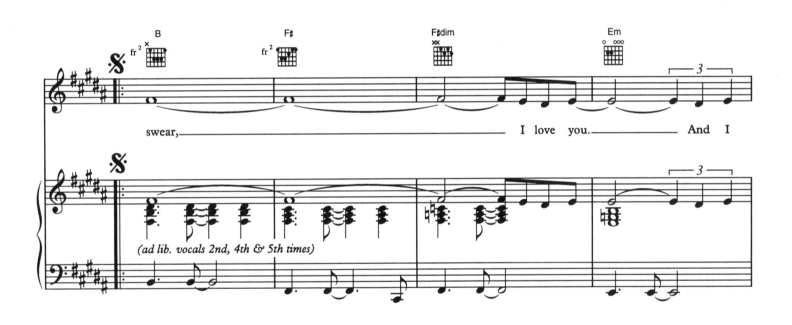

swear,_____ I love you._____ And I

(ad lib. vocals 2nd, 4th & 5th times)

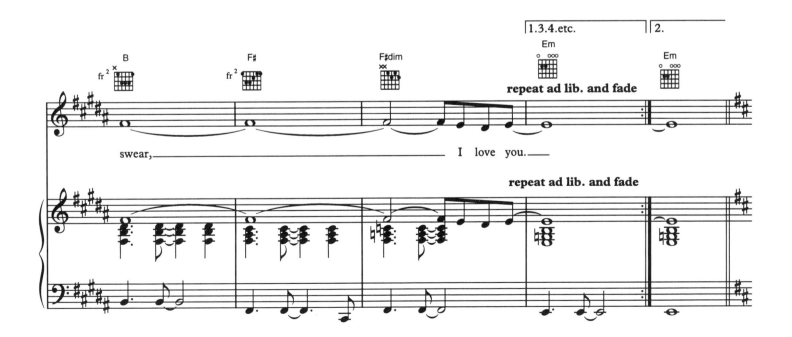

1.3.4.etc.   **2.**

repeat ad lib. and fade

swear,_____ I love you.____

repeat ad lib. and fade

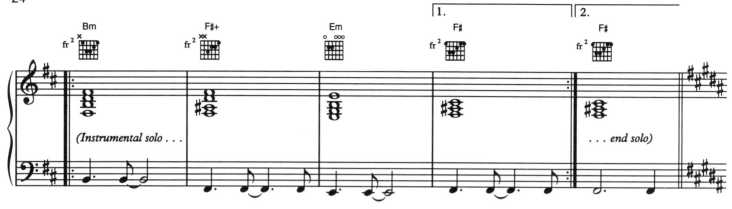

(Instrumental solo . . .   . . . end solo)

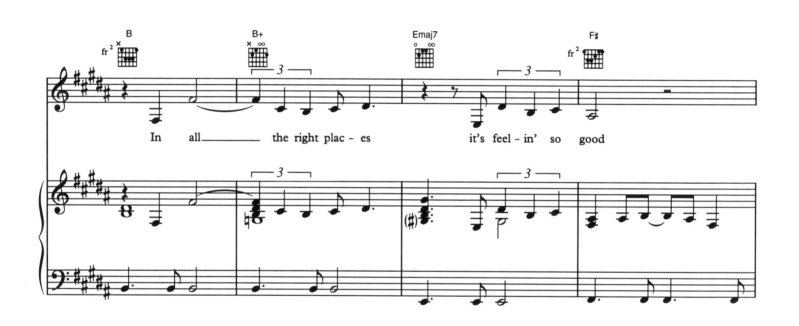

In all_____ the right plac - es   it's feel - in' so good

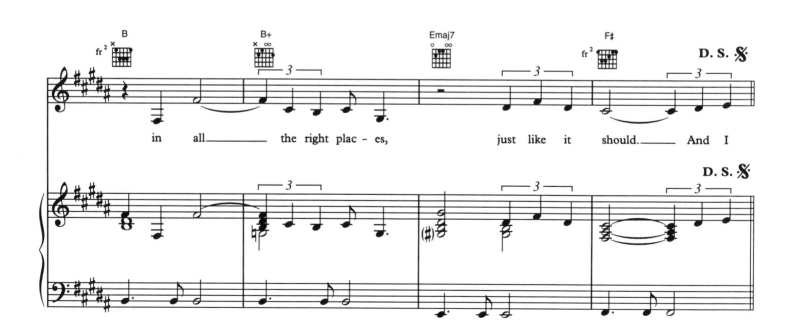

in all_____ the right plac - es,   just like it   should._____ And I

D. S. 𝄋

Goldfinger (from *Goldfinger*)

Words by Anthony Newley
and Leslie Bricusse
Music by John Barry

The Living Daylights
(from *The Living Daylights*)

Words by Pal Waaktaar
Music by John Barry and Pal Waaktaar

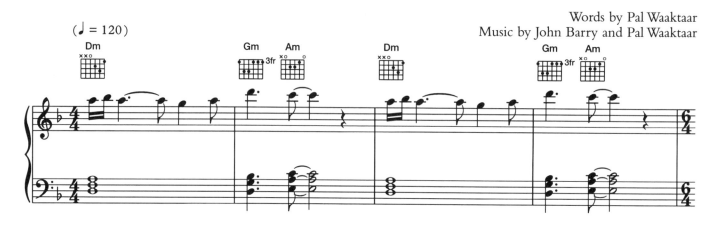

1. Hey dri - ver,
2. Al - right,

where we go - ing? I swear my nerves are show - ing. Set my hopes up way
hold on tight now, it's down, down to the wire.___ Set your hopes up way

Comes the morn - ing and__ the head - lights fade a - way.__

Hun-dred thou - sand peo - ple, I'm___ the_ one they frame._

Ah_____ the liv - ing day - lights._

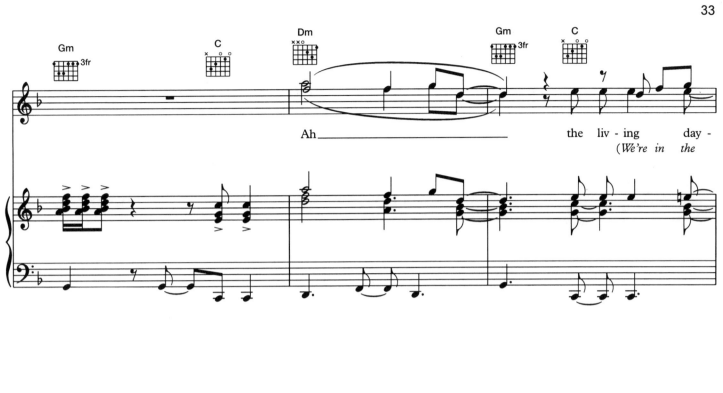

Ah _____ the liv-ing day-
(We're in the

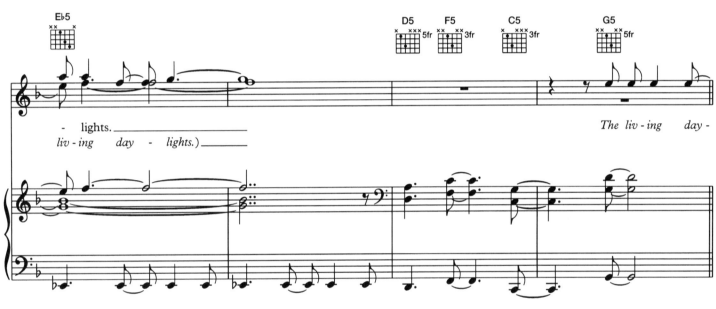

- lights. _____
liv-ing day - lights.) _____

The liv-ing day-

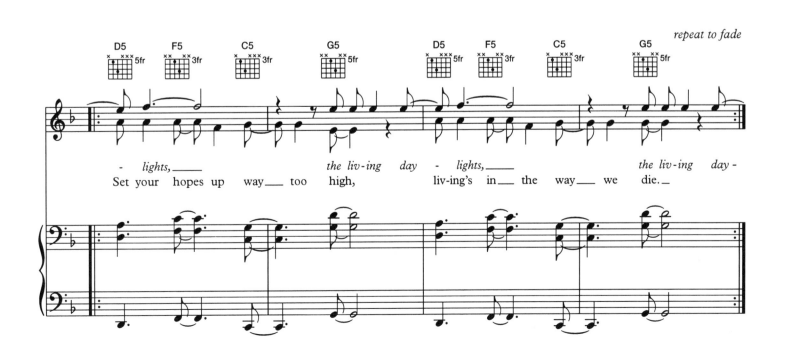

repeat to fade

- lights, _____ the liv-ing day - lights, _____ the liv-ing day-
Set your hopes up way___ too high, liv-ing's in___ the way___ we die. ___

The Man With The Golden Gun
(from *The Man With The Golden Gun*)

Words by Don Black
Music by John Barry

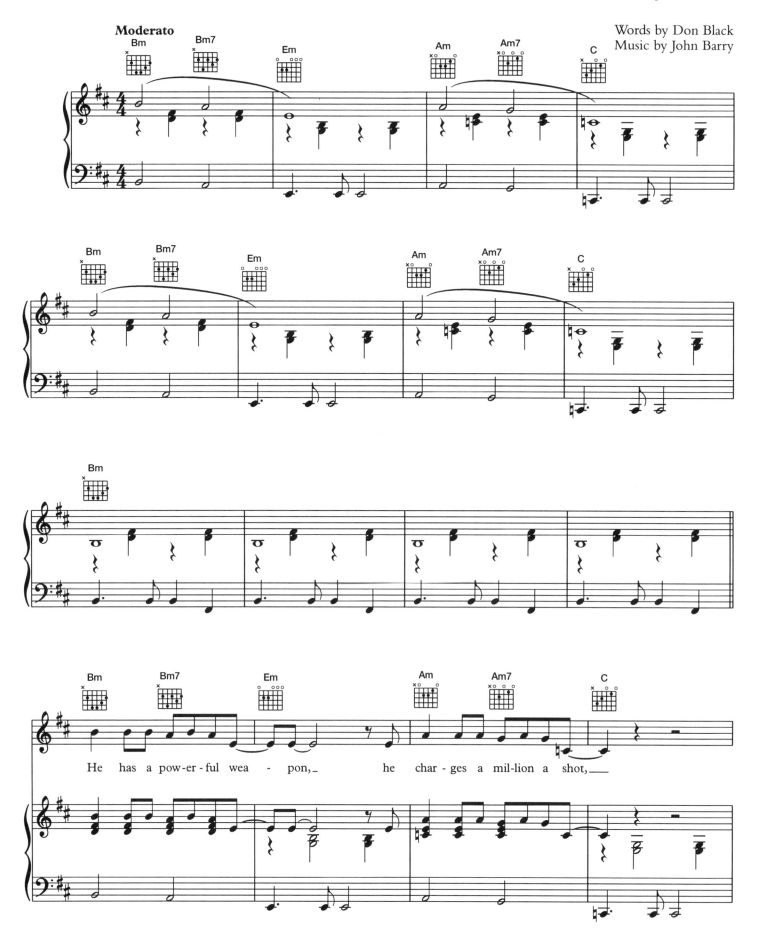

He has a pow-er-ful wea - pon,_ he char - ges a mil-lion a shot,___

Meadow Of Delight And Sadness
(from *The Beyondness Of Things*)

Music by John Barry

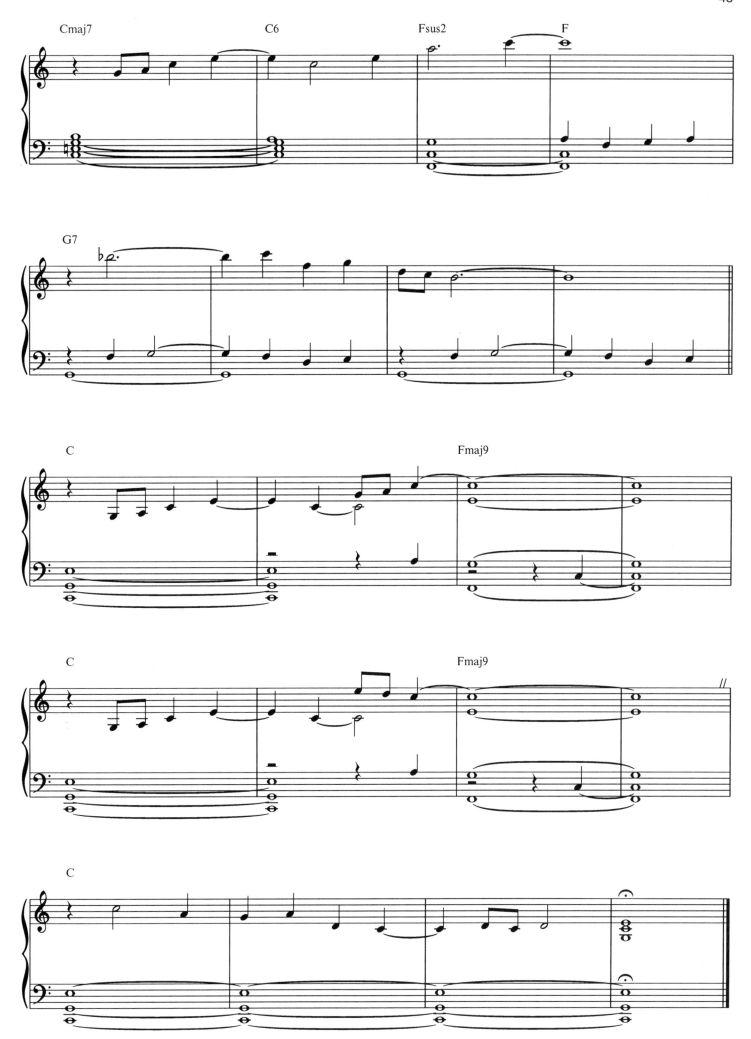

Thunderball (from *Thunderball*)

Words by Don Black
Music by John Barry

Verse 2:
He knows the meaning of success.
His needs are more, so he gives less.
They call him the winner who takes all.
And he strikes like Thunderball.

We Have All The Time In The World
(from *On Her Majesty's Secret Service*)

Words by Don Black
Music by John Barry

You Only Live Twice
(from *You Only Live Twice*)

Words by Leslie Bricusse
Music by John Barry

Moonraker (from *Moonraker*)

Words by Hal David
Music by John Barry

54

All
The Woman Series

All
Woman
volume one

Contents include: All Woman; Do You Know Where You're Going To?; Ev'ry Time We Say Goodbye;
Fever; I Am What I Am; I Will Always Love You; Miss You Like Crazy; Summertime;
Superwoman; What's Love Got To Do With It and Why Do Fools Fall In Love.
Order Ref: 19076

All
Woman
volume two

Contents include: Don't It Make My Brown Eyes Blue; Giving You The Best That I Got;
Killing Me Softly With His Song; Memory; One Moment In Time; Pearl's A Singer;
That Ole Devil Called Love; Walk On By; The Wind Beneath My Wings and You Don't Have To Say You Love Me.
Order Ref: 2043A

All
Woman
volume three

Contents include: Almaz; Big Spender; Crazy For You; Fame; The First Time Ever I Saw Your Face;
From A Distance; Love Letters; My Baby Just Cares For Me; My Funny Valentine; The Power Of Love;
Promise Me; Saving All My Love For You and Total Eclipse Of The Heart.
Order Ref: 2444A

All
Woman
volume four

Contents include: Anything For You; Evergreen; For Your Eyes Only; I Will Survive; Mad About The Boy;
A Rainy Night in Georgia; Send In The Clowns; Smooth Operator; Sophisticated Lady; Stay With Me Till Dawn;
Sweet Love; Think Twice and Touch Me In The Morning.
Order Ref: 3034A

All
Woman
Blues

Contents include: Body and Soul; Georgia On My Mind; God Bless' The Child;
I Don't Stand A Ghost Of A Chance With You; I Gotta Right To Sing The Blues; I'd Rather Go Blind;
Lover Man (Oh, Where Can You Be?); Mood Indigo; Stormy Weather and You've Changed.
Order Ref: 3690A

All
Woman
Cabaret

Contents include: Almost Like Being In Love; Another Openin', Another Show; Anything Goes;
For Once In My Life; Goldfinger; I Won't Last A Day Without You; If My Friends Could See Me Now;
My Way; New York New York; People and There's No Business Like Show Business.
Order Ref: 3691A

All
Woman
Jazz

Contents include: Bewitched; Crazy He Calls Me; A Foggy Day; Girl From Ipanema; How High The Moon;
I'm In The Mood For Love; It Don't Mean A Thing (If It Ain't Got That Swing); It's Only A Paper Moon;
Misty; On Green Dolphin Street; 'Round Midnight and Straighten Up And Fly Right.
Order Ref: 4778A